儿童情绪管理与性格培养绘本

I DON'T LOSE MY TEMPER

我不随便发脾气

胡媛媛 编

广东旅游出版社
GUANGDONG TRAVEL & TOURISM PRESS
中国·广州

图书在版编目（ＣＩＰ）数据

我不随便发脾气 / 胡媛媛编. —— 广州：广东旅游出版社, 2016.11
（儿童情绪管理与性格培养绘本）
ISBN 978-7-5570-0555-9

Ⅰ.①我… Ⅱ.①胡… Ⅲ.①儿童故事 – 图画故事 – 中国 – 当代 Ⅳ.①I287.8

中国版本图书馆 CIP 数据核字(2016)第 237793 号

总 策 划：罗艳辉
责任编辑：殷如筠
封面绘图：赵里骏
责任技编：刘振华
责任校对：李瑞苑

我 不 随 便 发 脾 气
WO BU SUIBIAN FA PIQI

广东旅游出版社出版发行
（广州市越秀区建设街道环市东路 338 号银政大厦西楼 12 楼　　邮编：510030）
邮购电话：020-87348243
广东旅游出版社图书网
www.tourpress.cn
湖北楚天传媒印务有限责任公司
（湖北省武汉市东湖新技术开发区流芳园横路 1 号　邮编：430205）
787 毫米 × 1092 毫米　16 开　2 印张　1 千字
2016 年 11 月第 1 版第 1 次印刷
定价：15.00 元

一只活泼任性的小猫叫亨利。

Henry was a lively and willful kitten.

清早，妈妈为亨利穿上一件蓝衬衣，亨利不喜欢。

In the morning, Mom dressed Henry in a blue shirt, but he didn't like it.

去幼儿园的路上，他的小嘴高高噘起。

He was pouting on the way to kindergarten.

幼儿

3

小狗托尼来找亨利，邀请他一起玩飞行棋。

Tony invited Henry to play the flight chess.

不一会儿，亨利上蹿下跳，烦躁不安——他输不起。

After a while, Henry fidgeted and jumped up and down. He was a poor loser.

"亨利，我又要起飞啦！"
托尼摇着尾巴很得意。

"Henry, I rolled a six again!" Tony
wagged his tail; he was pleased with
the game.

"嘭！哗啦！"亨利一抬手掀翻了棋盘，棋子落满地。

Bang! Crashed! Henry flipped the chessboard, and chess pieces fell on the ground.

托尼愣在一旁，惊讶地看着亨利，
然后"哇"的一声大哭起来。

Tony was stunned.
He looked at Henry in surprise and then burst into tears.

托尼的哭声引来了长颈鹿老师和其他的小伙伴。

Tony cried. Mr. Giraffe and kids gathered around him.

老师要求亨利向托尼道歉，还要捡起飞行棋。

Mr. Giraffe asked Henry to apologize to Tony and pick up chess pieces.

亨利气呼呼地站在那里，
胡须上下抖动，"呼哧呼哧"
很不服气。

*Henry was just standing there; his whiskers
quivered in outrage.*

长颈鹿老师拍了拍托尼的肩
膀，招呼他与小朋友们一起捡起
飞行棋。

*Mr. Giraffe patted on Tony's shoulde
and let kids to pick up chess pieces together*

孩子们又快乐地玩起了游戏。

Kids started to play happily again.

亨利独自在教室的一角，从这头走到那头，既孤独又无趣。

Henry was wandering around the classroom alone and felt lonely and bored.

亨利看见小兔和小松鼠在玩遥控车，要求与他们一起玩。

"我们不喜欢你乱发脾气！"他们拒绝了亨利。

Henry wanted to play with the toy car with Rabbit and Squirrel, but they refused, "we don't like your bad temper!"

小熊在搭积木，亨利慢慢
地向他移过去。

*Little Bear was playing with toy
bricks. Henry walked slowly toward
him.*

"你乱发脾气，没意思！"
小熊走开了，丢下积木和亨利。

"You have a bad temper. It's not fun!" Little Bear walked away from Henry and the toy bricks.

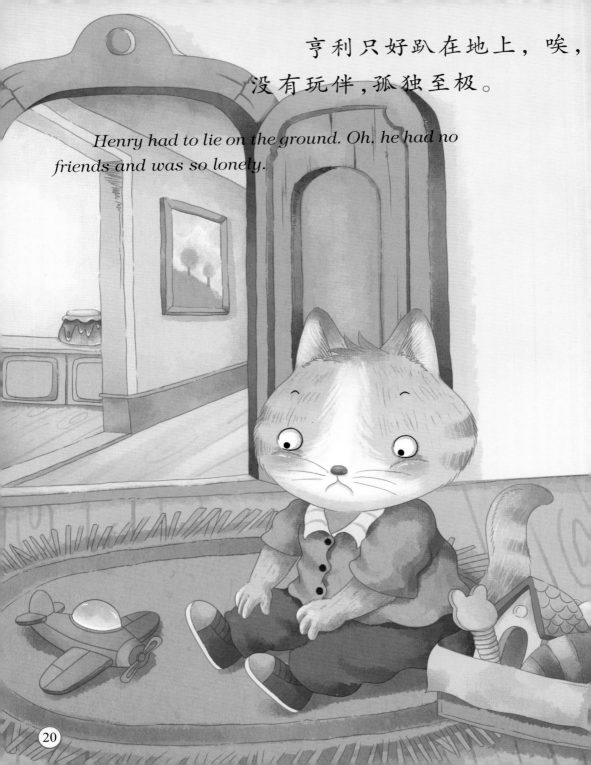

亨利只好趴在地上，唉，
没有玩伴，孤独至极。

*Henry had to lie on the ground. Oh, he had no
friends and was so lonely.*

他走到长颈鹿老师面前："老师，他们对我不理不睬。"

He came up to Mr. Giraffe. "Sir, they all leave me alone."

"为什么呢？"
"因为……因为……
我乱发脾气！"

"Why?" "Because...
because I lost my temper."

22

"还有呢？"
"我没有捡起飞行棋，更没有对托尼说对不起。"

"And?" *"I have neither picked up any chess pieces nor apologized to Tony."*

"你现在愿不愿意对托尼说对不起？"
"托尼能原谅我吗？大家还会不会与我一起玩？"

"Would you like to say sorry to Tony now?" "Will Tony forgive me? Are they going to play with me again?"

24

"只要你真心道歉，他们就会原谅你。记住今后不能乱发脾气。"

"Just apologize sincerely, and they will forgive you. Please remember to keep your temper in future."

"我记住了，老师！"亨利的脸涨得红红的。

"I got it, Sir,"
blushed Henry.

26

长颈鹿老师带着亨利来见托尼。"对不起,托尼,我不该掀翻飞行棋。我还想与你一起玩游戏。"

Mr. Giraffe took Henry to Tony. "I'm so sorry, Tony. I shouldn't have flipped the chessboard. I still want to play games with you, can we?"

托尼拉着亨利的手，笑眯眯："当然
一起玩！而且输赢都不许发脾气！"

"好，我一定不再随便发脾气！"

Tony took Henry's hand and smiled, "of course!
But whether you win or lose, don't lose your temper."
"OK, I will not do that again!"

"啪啪啪……"长颈鹿老师和小伙伴们使劲儿也鼓掌,因为亨利克服了坏脾气。

Mr. Giraffe and kids clapped heartily cause Henry managed to keep his temper.

给父母的话：

孩子年龄小，语言表达能力有限，所以常常会通过发脾气的方式来表达情绪。就像小亨利那样，有"噘嘴""烦燥不安""掀翻棋盘"" '呼哧呼哧'很不服气"等一系列行为出现。作为父母，应该及早重视孩子的情绪并做出正确的引导，帮助他们认识、了解和控制自己的情绪。

孩子发脾气、闹情绪都有不同的根源，而不同年龄阶段和心理特点的孩子表现情绪的方式也不同。怎样才能帮助孩子建立正确的情绪情感，做到不随便发脾气呢？

首先，家庭中要营造一种安全、平等、平和的氛围，家长要学会管理好自己的情绪，用正能量影响孩子，起到榜样的作用。其次，要让孩子学会认识情绪，愿意说出他（她）的想法与感受。家长只有知其情绪产生的原因，才能用正确的方法引导孩子学会控制不良情绪。再次，让孩子在游戏中，通过情境及角色的扮演感受别人的情绪，从而领悟积极情绪与消极情绪对同一件事产生的后果的区别。最后，家长应引导孩子乐观地生活，教会他们适当宣泄不良情绪的方法，避免大发脾气。比如：要发脾气时，不妨转移注意力，冷静一下，听听歌、跑跑步、做做操，或者干脆哭一场，这样就能把坏情绪释放出来。

在孩子发脾气、闹情绪时，家长切勿责备、打骂孩子，当然也不能坐视不管，一时的教育不当，不仅不利于孩子情绪的缓解，还会影响其今后的成长。学习如何正确地表达情绪，是我们和孩子一起努力的方向。